Earth

'*Moon colony is twenty-five years*
has used our minerals to make mo...
can't go on.'

Ann... ...Kepler live on Moon. Soon there will be big
change...
LEM...
middl...
follow...

Moni...
in Egy...
contin...
lives i...

Bef...
all the...
can b...
thinks...

Earthdark

MONICA HUGHES

Level 3

Retold by John Escott
Series Editor: Derek Strange

PENGUIN BOOKS

PENGUIN BOOKS

Published by the Penguin Group
Penguin Books Ltd, 27 Wrights Lane, London W8 5TZ, England
Penguin Books USA Inc., 375 Hudson Street, New York, New York 10014, USA
Penguin Books Australia Ltd, Ringwood, Victoria, Australia
Penguin Books Canada Ltd, 10 Alcorn Avenue, Toronto, Ontario, Canada M4V 3B2
Penguin Books (NZ) Ltd, 182–190 Wairau Road, Auckland 100, New Zealand

Penguin Books Ltd, Registered Offices: Harmondsworth, Middlesex, England

Earthdark © Monica Hughes 1977
First published by Hamish Hamilton Children's Books 1977
This adaptation published by Penguin Books 1995
10 9 8 7 6 5 4 3 2 1

Copyright © John Escott 1995
Illustrations copyright © Rodney Shaw (David Lewis Illustrators) 1995
All rights reserved

The moral right of the adapter and of the illustrator has been asserted

Illustrations by Rodney Shaw (David Lewis Illustrators)

Typeset by Datix International Limited, Bungay, Suffolk
Printed in England by Clays Ltd, St Ives plc
Set in 11/14 pt Monophoto Bembo

To the teacher:

In addition to all the language forms of Levels One and Two, which are used again at this level of the series, the main verb forms and tenses used at Level Three are:

- past continuous verbs, present perfect simple verbs, conditional clauses (using the 'first' or 'open future' conditional), question tags and further common phrasal verbs
- modal verbs: *have (got) to* and *don't have to* (to express obligation), *need to* and *needn't* (to express necessity), *could* and *was able to* (to describe past ability), *could* and *would* (in offers and polite requests for help), and *shall* (for future plans, offers and suggestions).

Also used are:

- relative pronouns: *who*, *that* and *which* (in defining clauses)
- conjunctions: *if* and *since* (for time or reason), *so that* (for purpose or result) and *while*
- indirect speech (questions)
- participle clauses.

Specific attention is paid to vocabulary development in the Vocabulary Work exercises at the end of the book. These exercises are aimed at training students to enlarge their vocabulary systematically through intelligent reading and effective use of a dictionary.

To the student:

Dictionary Words:

- When you read this book, you will find that some words are darker black than the others on the page. Look them up in your dictionary, if you do not already know them, or try to guess the meaning of the words first, without a dictionary.

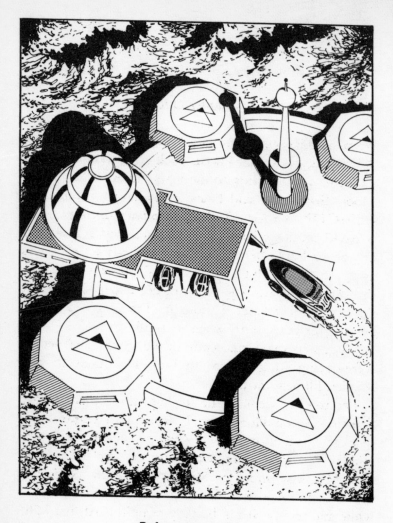

Before you read . . .

1 Look at the name of the story. What does it tell you about the *sort* of story you are going to read?

2 Look at the picture above. Where do you think it is?

Chapter One

It was midday when my father and I landed on Moon. After three months on **Earth**, it felt good to be back.

People were waiting to meet my father, who was the Moon **Governor**, and I saw Miles Fargo, the boss of LEMCON. LEMCON's business was **mining**.

And I could see Huntley Sheppard's grey head. It was his job to look after the **colony** while my father was away on Earth. But it took several minutes to realize that Ann Sheppard was not with her father. 'Why isn't she here to meet me?' I thought. 'I'm going to marry her in three years' time, when we finish school.'

My father was in the centre of the crowd, and people were trying to get close to him. He called to me, 'Kepler, I'll be some time.'

The tourists went to the **jet**-bus taking them to the Serenity Hilton Hotel, and I turned and climbed the stairs to the look-out room. Outside, under the bright midday sun, everything was white. It was forty years since Man first landed on Moon, back in the 1960s, but this was the way most Earth people remembered it – white and empty. It can be very beautiful. At first light the line between the dark and the bright blue side of Moon shines like a road covered with diamonds.

The sun was high behind me and the sky was crowded with stars of every colour. Earth was to the east of the sun, and hard to see without half-covering my eyes.

After some time I went downstairs again and saw people coming out of a room. Two heads were above the rest, my father's and Huntley Sheppard's. I pushed my way through.

'Dr Sheppard, where's Ann?' I wanted to know.

I sounded rude and he looked surprised. 'She's back at Kepler **Base**.'

'Why isn't she here to meet me? It's been three months.'

'Don't worry,' said Dr Sheppard. 'You'll see Ann soon enough.'

He turned and walked away, leaving me with a red face.

My father finally got away, and we rode in the Moon Car to Kepler Base. I left him working on some papers and went to speak to the driver.

'How have things been up here, Tim?' I asked.

'OK,' said Tim O'Connor. 'Your father's done some good work for us down at the United Nations, but I think LEMCON will make things difficult.'

'What can they do? The UN have said we can have our **independence** on Moon. Now LEMCON will have to do what we want.'

'The **miners** at Aristarchus are talking wildly,' said Tim. 'If Moon colony is to get some of the mining money now, it will come from the miners and not the LEMCON people back on Earth. There's talk that LEMCON will stop mining on Moon.'

'That's crazy,' I said. 'Earth needs our **minerals**.'

I went back to my father and repeated Tim's words.

'Tim O'Connor sounds like Miles Fargo,' my father said with a smile.

'LEMCON's boss?' I said. 'Was he angry?'

'He wasn't pleased. But he knew this had to happen. Moon colony is twenty-five years old, and for ten years LEMCON has used our minerals to make money and hasn't paid us a penny. It can't go on.'

We arrived at Kepler Base, and this time Ann *was* waiting for me.

'Ann, I'm so pleased to see you!' I said, and put my arms around her.

'Kep, everyone is looking at us!' she said.

'I'm sorry,' I said. 'But why didn't you come to meet me?'

She did not answer at first, but then she said, 'Kep, I don't know. I felt strange.'

She was very pretty and I was very lucky, I told myself.

'It's good to be home,' I said.

Good to be home! I told myself this again and again during the next moon day and night. But I got angry when I had to wait in the café, or when the shower water stopped before I was finished. And my small sleep-room began to feel like a prison. Again and again I thought about the large living-room of the house I stayed in on Earth. Everything in it had colour and was comfortable.

'Ann, you can remember Earth,' I said. 'It's only five years since you came up to Moon. Remember that, and then look at this place. I'm sure things could be better here.'

We were in the café. Forty white tables were in two lines. There were no flowers, no colour anywhere, only the green floor – the same green that was everywhere on the Base. I hated that colour green.

9

'Yes, I can remember Earth,' said Ann. 'Crowds of people, all fighting for the things that were left. I'm glad I'm on Moon.'

Things were not right between Ann and me. Two days later she told me she was moving over to 'B' Watch; I was on 'A' Watch. For eight out of every twenty-four hours, one-third of the people on the Base slept. Of the twelve hundred people there, most of us only knew the four hundred people on our own Watch. We almost never saw the other two Watches.

I looked at her. 'But why?'

Her face went red. 'Guy Roget is giving some special lessons. I can't go to them if I stay on "A" Watch, but I can if I'm on "B".'

'She's being polite,' I thought sadly. 'She really wants to get away from me.'

♦

I didn't see Ann again until the New Day came. The children of all three Watches had a party every New Day – twelve or thirteen times a year, when two weeks of day began after two weeks of night. We were in the café, the only room big enough for the party, and I was with 'A' Watch.

I saw Ann dancing with a boy I didn't know – one of her new friends from 'B' Watch, I guessed. I broke in on them without asking and started dancing with Ann.

'Happy New Day, Ann!' I said.

'Happy New Day, Kep.'

We danced silently for a few minutes, then I pulled her off the floor.

*'Look. There's a two-man Moon Car parked outside that
air-lock door. Let's go for a drive, Ann!'*

'Where are we going?' she said.

'To the look-out room,' I said. 'I want to talk to you
alone.'

From there we looked down on to the **crater** floor,
and suddenly I wanted to be right out there, to be part
of Moon.

I pointed at a shadow. 'Look. There's a two-man
Moon Car parked outside that air-lock door. Let's go
for a drive, Ann!'

'You know you have to ask your father first,' she
said.

'He's away. By the time I see him it will probably be
the middle of the night again. You ask your father.'

'No,' she said. 'I don't want to.'

I became angry. 'OK, then! I'll go by myself.'

'Kep, you *are* crazy!' she said. 'If you go outside I – I'll have to tell the Base guards.'

'That's for you to decide,' I said. 'But give me a little time.'

I went into the changing-room and put on my **space-suit**, then I pushed the switch to open the air-lock door to get to the Moon Car. Moon Cars have clear plastic covers and they move with small jets. We use them as taxis for short journeys across Moon.

I got behind the controls. A minute later the car was moving slowly across the crater floor. I'll drive a hundred miles north and a hundred miles back, I thought. Two hours out here alone, to think about things.

The sun was white and hot against the side of the Moon Car. Almost an hour and a hundred miles later, the car's radio broke into my silent journey.

'Sun-storm warning!' came the voice. 'All **surface** workers return to Base immediately! The storm will hit Kepler Crater in fifty minutes. I repeat, return to Base immediately, all surface workers!'

I tried to think. Sun-storms hit Moon with danger-ously strong **radiation**. The radiation can easily kill. I had to find cover quickly or die; but I was an hour's journey from Kepler Base and it meant driving straight into the storm. North-west was Aristarchus – three hours' drive instead of one, but Aristarchus was still in night, away from the sun, and maybe I could get to the LEMCON base there before the storm hit Moon.

I turned the car to the north-west, towards Aristarchus and LEMCON base.

Chapter Two

It was a terrible drive, and I was very frightened. You can't see a sun-storm. They aren't like other storms at all. If a storm catches you, you don't know it until it is too late. You don't feel a thing, but after a few hours you start to feel sick and weak. And some time after that, you die.

I drove on into the dark, watching for small craters and other dangers. 'It can't be far now,' I told myself. And then I saw a light in the darkness. It was Aristarchus! I was there! But only just in time.

Aristarchus was a large crater, twenty-nine miles wide. As I got near it I could see the lights of machines. So this was LEMCON, who took all the important minerals out of Moon and paid us nothing. LEMCON did not like people from the colony to come here, and I felt like a criminal sitting in the Moon Car and looking down into the crater. All the machines were going one way, and I realized that the drivers were going below ground because of the storm that was coming. I knew that I must do the same, and I drove my car down into the crater.

Suddenly, two bright lights shone straight at me and a great big machine came my way. The two lights became four, the four became eight, all going round and round . . . and suddenly everything went black.

I knew nothing after that until I found someone

pulling me through an air-lock door. Hands pulled off my space-suit and someone gave me some water before I dropped on to a wonderfully soft bed and slept.

I woke up to see the cold grey eyes of a man looking at me. He was on the other side of a glass door, about five feet away. He was fat and his hair was almost white. Another man was next to him. The other man had red hair and blue eyes. They were talking, but I couldn't hear through the glass door. *But I could read their lips.* Moon children learn to do some strange things, and lip-reading is one of them. The two men never knew it, but I could *see* almost every word they said.

The fat man said, 'You were a fool to bring him in here, Blue.'

'I couldn't leave him out in the sun-storm, Clint,' said the other man.

'There's no place in LEMCON for soft hearts,' said the fat man.

'I'm getting out of here soon,' said Blue. 'I'm tired of living under the ground like an animal. And we're taking minerals out so fast and working long hours –'

'LEMCON's nearly finished,' said Clint, 'and Miles Fargo's got his orders. We have to get all we can before the UN people get here and stop us.'

'So why worry about the boy? When the UN people arrive *they'll* see the things that Fargo's done here.'

'If the UN don't know that we've done anything wrong, they won't hurry up here. We'll have a year to clean up, maybe more. But the boy saw the number of machines and perhaps he knows we've got the Nulli-fiers.'

'What do we do, Clint?' said Blue.

'Kill him, of course.'

I shut my eyes and tried to stop shaking. The door opened and a hand was suddenly on my shoulder. I turned and looked up at the two men.

'Get up!' the fat man said. His voice was soft, almost a whisper.

I stood up and looked round. There was only the bed in the small white room. The room on the other side of the glass door was an office, with a desk and chairs. The door of the office was shut.

'What's your name? Where are you from?' the soft voice asked.

'Kepler . . .' I began, then I stopped.

I tried to think. Perhaps the radios weren't working because of the radiation storm. Perhaps nobody was asking about Kepler Masterman, son of the Moon Governor. I must make them believe that I'm nobody important and it's all a mistake, I thought, then maybe they'll let me go.

'. . . I'm from Kepler Base,' I went on. 'My name is Eric Erickson.'

'Why are you here? Kepler Base is four hundred miles away.'

I told them about the New Day party and taking the Moon Car.

Clint listened and said, 'Watch him, Blue.' Then he left the room.

I suddenly felt sick.

'Are you all right, boy?' Blue asked, when he saw my white face.

I sat down on the bed. 'The radiation . . . was I outside for long?'

'No,' he said. 'I got you inside ten minutes before the storm hit us.'

'I can't remember . . . Where was I when you found me?'

'On the crater floor,' said Blue.

He was looking at me strangely when Clint came back.

'There is an Eric Erickson,' he said. 'Fifteen years old, and he's lived on Kepler Base for three years.'

'Five years,' I said.

Clint smiled. 'Five, yes,' he said, and I knew he was testing me.

Blue left the room and came back a few minutes later with some hot food. He put it in front of me. Then the fat man left the room again.

'When did you last eat a meal like this?' asked Blue.

'When I was on Earth,' I said, with my mouth full of hot potatoes. 'We eat dried food at Kepler. It doesn't taste as good as this.'

'This only comes out of a tin,' said Blue. 'It's nothing wonderful.'

'A *tin*!' I said. 'Tins of food are very expensive to get from Earth. How do you get them up here?'

He looked surprised by my question. 'By carrier, of course. Carriers go down to Earth full of minerals and come back with our food.'

'Why can't you bring food from Earth for the colony people too?'

'We could, if you paid us,' said Blue.

I was angry. 'We were here for fifteen years before LEMCON. We helped you build the machines for your work. Now we have to pay you so much for our

Blue left the room and came back a few minutes later with some hot food. He put it in front of me.

water and we don't even have enough for a shower! And after we've paid for the air we need there's no money left for good food or nice furniture. Yet LEMCON pays us *nothing*!' I pushed my plate away. 'But when the UN comes you'll *have* to pay.'

Suddenly the door crashed open and Clint ran into the room. He hit me across the face. 'You lied, boy!' he shouted. 'The radio is working again. You're not Eric Erickson. It was the Governor's son, Kepler Masterman, who took a Moon Car and disappeared before the storm.' He turned to Blue. 'That's who we have here, the Moon Governor's boy!'

'What — what are we going to do?' said Blue. He looked afraid. 'He hasn't seen the Nullifiers, and he can't remember a thing, Clint. Why don't we just give him to the boss?'

'Fargo will give him to his father,' said Clint. 'The men *I* work for will want this boy dead.'

'But he didn't see anything, Clint. He can't remember anything.'

'There are the Nullifiers,' said the fat man. 'He'll talk about them and then we'll be in trouble. No, we have to kill him, Blue.'

Chapter Three

We went through a **tunnel**. Would they kill me here, inside LEMCON? I tried to run — but a strong hand came down on my arm and held me. It pushed me into a lift and we began to go up.

Clint was holding a gun and was pointing it at me.

I saw that he had a scar on his face. His eyes met mine for a second.

The lift doors opened and we went out into another tunnel. Some men were coming towards us, but I felt Clint's gun in my back and I could do nothing. The men pushed past us. They looked tired and dirty, and one almost fell against me. I looked at him. I saw that he had a **scar** on his face. His eyes met mine for a second, then the men were past us and we were at some cupboards.

Clint opened one and took out a big Earth spacesuit. 'Put it on,' he told me.

'I can't wear that,' I said. 'It's too big and heavy.'

His hand went up to hit me, but Blue stopped him. 'Wait, Clint. We don't want them to find the boy in one of our suits, do we?'

Clint's arm dropped to his side. 'What did you do with the boy's spacesuit?'

Blue opened another cupboard and took out my spacesuit. I put it on while they put on their heavy suits. Then we went through an air-lock door and out on to the surface of Moon.

Clint and I got into my Moon Car and we crossed the floor of the crater. Clint drove the car. It was new to him and it took him some time to understand the way to drive it. I didn't help him. Blue followed us in one of the other machines.

We were nearly a hundred miles out from Aristarchus before the sun shone straight at the car. Suddenly it was so bright that Clint could not see for a second or two. I shouted, 'Look out! Quick, turn! Don't you see it?' and I pulled the wheel from his hands while he tried to cover his eyes from the sun.

The car ran straight into a small **dust** crater and stopped.

'Too late!' I said. 'You didn't see it, did you?'

'It was the sun! I couldn't see a thing – only the sun!' Clint shouted angrily, but he could not get the car out again.

A minute later Blue came up behind us in the LEMCON machine.

'How do we get this thing out of here?' Clint asked me.

I pretended to be very frightened. 'I don't know. You need another Moon Car or a machine to pull you out. Moon Cars usually travel in pairs, it's safer.'

It was a lie: Moon Cars travelled alone. And they did not need anything to pull them out of small dust craters, but Clint did not know that. I could see him getting an idea.

'Travel together, do they? But you wanted to be alone, didn't you, Kepler Masterman?' He smiled. 'Well, you will be!' And he opened the door of the car and got out.

'Wait! Use your machine to pull the car out!' I shouted, pretending to be more frightened than before. 'You can't leave me here alone! I'll use up all my air and die!'

Clint just smiled again and walked away towards the machine that Blue was driving. I watched him get in next to Blue, and then their machine turned round and went back to Aristarchus.

When it was gone I smiled and moved over to the controls. I pushed some switches and after a few seconds the Moon Car very slowly moved out of the small crater through clouds of dust.

Minutes later I was travelling towards Kepler Base.

♦

Base guards were waiting for me.

'I have to talk to my father,' I told them. 'It's very important.'

My father was sitting behind his desk and he looked very tired. 'Why did you do it, Kepler?' he said.

'I – I don't know,' I said. 'I'm sorry, father. I just had to get away . . .'

'Where have you been?'

'To Aristarchus,' I said. And I told him about Clint and Blue.

He listened, then he said, 'And Clint called that thing a *Nullifier*, did he?'

'Yes,' I said.

'You must say nothing about this to anyone. Do you promise me that?'

'I promise,' I said. 'But what *is* a Nullifier? And why aren't you surprised that LEMCON –?'

'You were wrong to take that Moon Car, Kepler, you know that,' he cut in quickly, without answering my questions. 'You will stay on the Base until the next New Day, do you understand?'

'Yes, father,' I said quietly.

Something was going on that my father was not telling me about, I thought. Some important secret. But what was it?

♦

Before the next New Day arrived, Ann came to see me. She looked tired and worried.

'Kep, you've got to help me,' she said. 'My father's disappeared.'

'Your Dad? Disappeared?' I said. 'What do you mean?'

'I haven't seen him since the last New Day, almost two weeks ago. He's not at home or at his office. His secretary tells everyone that he's sick, but it's not true.'

'Perhaps he's in the hospital,' I said.

'He isn't,' answered Ann. 'He's not anywhere on the Base.'

'Then he's in some other place on Moon,' I said.

'He isn't. I've asked everywhere and nobody has seen him. Something terrible has happened to him, Kep, I know it has!'

'What does your mother say?' I asked.

'She says, if his secretary says he's at home sick, then he's at home sick. Then she goes back to her work. It's impossible to talk to her,' said Ann. 'But *I* think someone has kidnapped him.'

'Kidnapped him! Who do you think has kidnapped him?'

'I don't know,' said Ann. 'Maybe LEMCON. They're really angry that the UN are going to make them pay us money for the minerals.'

'If they kidnap anybody, it'll be my father,' I said. '*He* was the one who talked with the UN. Have you talked to him?'

'Yes,' she answered. 'He said, "Why don't you listen to your mother, Ann, and leave things alone? It'll be best for your father, and you." It means something bad has happened to Daddy, Kep, I know it does!' She dropped her voice to a whisper. 'And I've searched Daddy's room.'

'Searched it?'

'Yes, and I found this.' She took a piece of paper from her pocket.

'It's just a Moon map,' I said.

'Kep, look at the line on it,' said Ann. 'It goes straight to Earthdark!'

I looked again and saw that she was right. From Kepler Base, a broken line went west-north-west straight into the place people on Earth call 'the dark side of the Moon'. We call it Earthdark, because it always looks dark from Earth. It is completely empty, like a desert. There were no bases there and nobody lived there.

'I think that's where they've taken Daddy,' said Ann.

'But nobody lives in Earthdark.'

'Look at the map, Kep,' she said. 'The line starts with an "X" here at Kepler Crater and ends with another "X" out there in Earthdark. And I found the map in Daddy's sleep-room, hidden under a cupboard. It was only with luck that I found it.'

'But who took him? And why?' I said. 'There's no colony over there, and LEMCON don't have any mines there.'

'But Daddy *has* disappeared,' said Ann. 'And he *did* hide the map in his room, and it *does* have an "X" on Earthdark. Please help me, Kep!'

'OK,' I said. 'What do you want me to do?'

'I want you to come with me. I want us to follow the line on that map.'

'Into Earthdark? That's crazy!' I said. 'Do you know how far it is?'

'Twelve hundred miles,' she said.

'Yes, and twelve hundred miles back,' I said. 'We can't take a Moon Car, they won't travel that far.'

'We don't have to, there's another way. I'll tell you later.'

It was time for me to go to my lessons. 'Let me take the map,' I said. 'I'll talk to my father – he'll listen to me.'

♦

After my lesson I went up to my father's office. There was someone with him and I had to wait. I heard voices on the other side of the door, and I heard one clearly.

'. . . *if you don't, Dr Sheppard will be in trouble, I warn you!*' Dr Sheppard – Ann's father!

Then the door opened and a man hurried out of the

office. There was a scar on his face and, for a second, our eyes met. His eyes got wider when he saw me. In another second he was gone.

'What is it, Kepler?' my father said. 'I haven't much time.'

My hand touched the map in my pocket. I thought about the man with the scar. Did I know him?

'Who was that man?' I asked. 'He doesn't live on Kepler, but I'm sure I've seen him before.'

'Perhaps you have,' answered my father. 'He's been on Moon for eighteen days, to talk with me. He's with the UN.' My father spoke smoothly. He never lied to me. *So why didn't I believe him?*

The UN ... LEMCON ... Aristarchus ... And then I remembered! I saw Scarface among the miners at LEMCON! And he knew me a minute ago! I thought, remembering the way his eyes widened.

'Kep, are you all right?' my father was saying.

'What? Yes ... yes. He's from the UN, you said, and one of the people you met down on Earth. And he's been in Kepler since last midnight – eighteen days ago?'

'Yes, we're working together. Kep, did you want to see me about something important?'

'It's OK, father, I'll talk to you another time,' I said.

I hurried away to my sleep-room. My head was full of questions. Why was my father lying to me? Scarface was not at Kepler Base eighteen days ago, because I saw him in Aristarchus. Why lie for a LEMCON man? And what was a LEMCON man doing in Kepler? ... *if you don't, Dr Sheppard will be in trouble, I warn you!* Perhaps LEMCON was holding Ann's father? Was

Scarface here to make sure that my father didn't talk?

I had to wait two hours to see Ann because she was at her lessons with the rest of the 'B' Watch students. When she saw me she looked excited.

'Kep! You'll do it? You'll come to Earthdark?'

'Yes,' I said.

'Why did you decide to come?' she asked.

'I don't want to talk about that now, Ann,' I said. 'We can't take a Moon Car, but you said there was another way.'

'Yes, there's a special new jet carrier that will go three thousand miles,' said Ann.

'A new jet carrier?' I said, very surprised. 'I've never heard a word about it.'

'There are only three of them,' said Ann. 'I've seen them.'

'Where?'

'Hidden in a secret garage under the north-west side of the crater.'

'Hidden?' I said. 'How did you find them?'

'The map showed me the way. Look at the first "X" on Kepler,' she said. 'It's in the north-west corner. That's where the secret garage is.'

I looked at the 'X' and saw that she was right. 'OK,' I said, 'so we can get one of these new jet carriers. We'll need enough food and water for four days – two days out and two days back.'

'More,' she said. 'We'll have Daddy on the way back.'

Did she really believe that we could find her father? I hoped she was right. If we can get Dr Sheppard back from LEMCON and help my father, I told myself, then I'll be happy to make the dangerous journey out into Earthdark.

Chapter Four

Ann and I met at 0300 hours on the fourth day of the moon night.

The three jet carriers were in the hidden garage under the side of the crater. They had tins of food and bottles of water in them already. I chose the one nearest the exit. The carrier was bigger and stronger than a Moon Car, but why was it still a *secret*? I didn't understand.

Stars shone above us as we moved across Moon surface, and Earth was dark red against the black sky. We went west-north-west, slowly starting to see more easily in the starlight and earth-shine, so that I didn't need to switch on the lights. After two hours the surface became rougher. Ann was looking at the map and making sure that we were going the right way.

'Look, another car was here,' I said, pointing at the moon-dust on the ground in front of us. 'It went west, straight into Earthdark.'

We looked at the wheel-lines in the moon-dust.

'We'll follow them,' said Ann. 'It'll be easier.' She looked excited. 'Kep, it *is* Daddy. I was right. The map was right!'

'Don't get too excited,' I told her. 'Perhaps it was another person.' I was secretly worried that we would find a broken-down car with a dead Dr Sheppard inside it.

We travelled for another three hours, then stopped to

have a meal and a few hours' sleep. After that, we moved on quickly again – but only for fifty miles, when the ground got rougher and rougher and I had to slow down. The next two hundred miles passed slowly. Then, quite suddenly, we could not see Earth any more. We were in Earthdark! Earth was always in the sky above Kepler Base, but suddenly it wasn't there. It felt very strange.

'Kepler, look!' Ann was pointing at something bright, up in the sky in front of us.

I stopped the car and looked. 'It's a **satellite**,' I said, 'right above the centre of Earthdark. Who put it there?'

'Why have a radio satellite when nobody lives over here?'

'Perhaps there *are* people living and working over here,' I said. 'Enough people to need a radio satellite.'

'But who?' said Ann.

'People who don't like the way we live on Kepler Base?' I said.

'Not Daddy,' said Ann. 'Which means that somebody is using him, doesn't it? LEMCON perhaps?' She sounded afraid.

I remembered Scarface at the door of my father's office, and my father's lies about him. And I remembered that Scarface was a LEMCON man. 'LEMCON, yes,' I said.

We drove on and Ann kept her eyes on the map. After another eighty miles she said, 'We must be above it now.'

'Whatever *it* is,' I said. We were in a big crater, sixty miles wide. The 'X' on the map was on the middle of the west wall. 'I'll go outside and take a look,' I said.

'Kelper, look!' Ann was pointing at something bright in the
sky in front of us.

'We go together, Kep, or we don't go at all,' said Ann.

We went out into the black night of Earthdark, and waited until our eyes could see in the dark before we moved towards the crater wall. There, in the wall of the crater, we found a shining new air-lock door. I opened it and we drove into a dark garage. I shut the outside door and found the switch to start the air machine. Soon we were able to take off our suits and breathe easily. I opened the inside door and we went through into a tunnel, eight or ten feet long and with lights in the ceiling. At the end was darkness.

We moved into the tunnel, and suddenly the door behind us *shut itself*.

Together we tried to open it again, but we could not move it.

'Kep, we can't get back!' said Ann.

We moved on into the darkness at the end of the tunnel. Suddenly someone shone a light straight into my face. I heard Ann cry out.

'Take your hands off her!' I shouted.

A soft voice spoke in my ear. 'Do everything I tell you, boy, and your girl will be all right. OK?' I knew that voice. It was the fat man, Clint.

'OK,' I said.

'Good,' he said. 'Blue, turn on the lights. Harris, go and look at the air-lock door.'

Lights went on above my head and I looked round. It was a small room. There were sleeping-bags on the floor, a table and two chairs, and at the back were some boxes with food in them.

Clint was looking at us, the gun in his hand again,

and Blue went and stood near him. I pulled Ann close to me. We could hear feet hurrying back along the tunnel, and the two men looked past us when the man called Harris came back.

'The door is locked,' said Harris.

'Didn't you hear them come in?' said Clint angrily.

'I heard nothing,' said Harris.

Clint put the gun in his pocket. 'So we meet again, young Masterman. You seem to be very lucky at staying alive.'

'My father knows that you tried to kill me before,' I said. 'If you try anything again –'

'Me?' said Clint. 'My dear boy, this time we're *all* in trouble.'

'What are you talking about?'

'The air-lock door,' said Blue.

'You mean it wasn't you who closed it?' I said. 'Then who –?'

'That's a good question,' said Blue.

'How did you get here?' I said. 'Were you following us?'

'Don't be stupid,' said Blue. 'We had a map.'

'Shut up, Blue!' said the fat man. 'You talk too much. We'll ask the questions, young Masterman. How did *you* get here?'

'We had a map too.' I took it from my pocket and gave it to Clint.

'It's the same! How did they get this, Harris?'

'I don't know,' said Harris. 'That's the real map, I just took a photo of it. Perhaps they found it in Dr Sheppard's room, in the same place that I found it. I left it there, you know that.'

31

Ann jumped forward angrily, her fingers cutting into his face, so that blood ran down the left side of it. 'What have you done with my father?'

They pushed her back towards me, and Clint looked at Harris. 'What's she talking about?'

Harris turned and I saw all of his face for the first time. I saw the scar. 'Scarface!' I was so surprised, I said it out loud.

Blue pushed between us. 'What's going on? You two know each other, do you? What's all this about the girl's father? Who is he?'

'He works for the Governor,' said Ann. She pointed at Scarface Harris. 'I think *he* kidnapped my father. It's the only way he could have that map. It was in my father's sleep-room.'

'The girl's crazy, Blue,' said Harris.

Clint was holding his gun again, but now he was pointing it at Harris. 'How interesting that the boy seems to know you. Where did you meet?'

'The last time I saw him,' I said before Harris could speak, 'he was talking with my father. They seemed very friendly.' I wanted to make trouble for Scarface. He was the kidnapper of Ann's father, I was sure.

Clint moved fast. He hit Harris over the head with the gun and Harris fell to the ground. Ann screamed.

Clint put the gun away. 'Tie him up, Blue,' he ordered. 'Then tie up the boy. The girl can cook us a meal.'

Blue tied my arms behind me, then pushed me into a corner of the room with Harris. Ann began to look through the boxes of food.

'Who are they?' she whispered to me. 'How did you know them?'

*Clint moved fast. He hit Harris over the head with the gun,
and Harris fell to the ground.*

'LEMCON men,' I whispered back. 'I'll tell you
later.'

Ann made a meal with Moon food.

'It's food for pigs, this Moon food!' said Blue.

Ann helped me to eat, because my hands were tied.
Harris lay with his eyes closed. Blue and Clint sat at the
table with their backs to us.

'Are we going to sit here until we've no air or water
left?' said Blue.

'People use this place,' said Clint. 'Somebody will
come soon, and this time we'll be ready for them.'

Then Ann and I noticed that Harris was waking up.
The blood on his face was dry now, but it was a bad cut.

Ann moved closer to him and gave him some water. He whispered something to her.

She turned and whispered to me, 'He says he can get us out.'

'OK,' I whispered back. 'But don't untie him.'

Ann made sure that Clint and Blue were still turned the other way, then she put her hand into Harris's coat pocket. She took out a small green bottle. Harris whispered, and I saw his lips say, '. . . in their next meal. But don't eat any of it yourselves.'

Later, Ann made another meal for Clint and Blue, this time with meat and vegetables from a tin. 'What's in the green bottle?' I thought. 'Is she going to put it in their meal?' I saw her do it before she carried the plates of hot food over to Clint and Blue.

Ann and I ate some Moon food, Ann helping me again. After some time the room became very quiet. Blue's head dropped on to the table, his long arms by his sides. Clint was sitting in his chair with his eyes closed.

'They won't wake up for three hours or more,' said Harris, his eyes wide open now. 'Untie me.'

'No!' I said to Ann. 'Don't untie him until we know more.'

'What will you do with us?' Ann asked Harris.

'Take you to . . . to a safe place,' he said.

'Why didn't you go before, if you know how to open the door?' I asked.

'After all the trouble I had bringing Clint and Blue here with that map?'

Then Ann untied us and helped Harris to stand up. 'I'm sorry I cut your face,' she said.

He put his hand up to the cut. 'It's all right,' he said.

He took Clint's gun, put on one of the heavy space-suits, then went down the tunnel towards the air-lock door. We followed him.

'Kepler, help Ann up so that she can touch the light above the door,' said Harris. 'Now . . . just above the light, there's a small switch . . . yes, there . . . push it twice. And . . . *open.*'

The door opened and the three of us went into the garage air-lock between that door and the outside door. Ann and I put on our spacesuits. Harris closed the door behind us; Clint and Blue were prisoners again. A minute later we were outside on the surface of Moon again.

Chapter Five

'I'll travel with you,' Harris said, and we got into our jet carrier.

'Who are you?' asked Ann. 'You didn't kidnap my father, did you?'

'No,' said Harris. 'People on Earth sent me here. LEMCON people, yes, but the people who want to know what is *really* happening in Aristarchus.'

'Not the people whom Clint and Blue work for?' I said.

'No, not them,' he said. 'But you saw me in Aristarchus and I had to move quickly. I asked your father to help me catch Clint and Blue somewhere away from Aristarchus: the last thing I wanted was to make trouble among the miners. So your father gave me a photo of the map. It's a photo of the real map, but it's got nothing to do with any of this.'

'How did the real map get into Dr Sheppard's room?' I asked. 'Why was it hidden, if it wasn't important?'

'I didn't know – and I still don't know – if Clint and Blue have someone working for them inside Kepler Base,' said Harris. 'I told them that I found the real map hidden in Dr Sheppard's room, so it had to be there if someone looked. Your father hid it for me, Kepler, but we didn't know that *you two* would find it!'

I felt my face getting red. 'So the map doesn't mean anything; it was just something to bring Clint and Blue here. And we followed it all the way to Earthdark for *nothing*.'

'What will happen to us now?' asked Ann. 'Are you taking us back to Kepler Base?'

'No,' said Harris. 'I don't have the time.' He switched on the radio in the car and began to speak into it. 'Hallo, Genesis One, this is Loner. Can I bring in two visitors? . . . No, not them. They're sleeping, the way we planned . . . Yes. Kepler Masterman and Ann Sheppard . . . Yes, I did say that . . . I'll send them in. Goodbye, Genesis One.' He turned to me. 'All right if I drive, Kepler?'

'OK,' I said.

'You're still not quite sure that I'm your friend, are you?' he said.

'No, perhaps I'm not,' I said. 'When you were in my father's office I thought you were a kidnapper.'

He laughed. 'Well, it was an easy mistake for you to make after Ann said that she thought somebody kidnapped her father. But I was telling your father that Clint was getting too close to Dr Sheppard's plans for Moon colony. I told him that I had to get Clint and Blue out of the way, and that it was important that he gave me the photo of the map. *That's* when I said, "If you don't, Dr Sheppard will be in trouble, I warn you!"'

'So Dr Sheppard isn't missing and our journey was a waste of time,' I said. 'I feel really stupid.'

'It was still brave of you to come all the way out here into Earthdark,' said Harris.

He started the car and I went to sit behind him with Ann, then he drove us across the crater to another part of the wall. He stopped.

'There's an air-lock door in the wall in front of you,' he said. 'Go through it and follow the tunnel. You'll find another lock at the other end. You know the way to open and shut them now. Goodbye.'

'Will we see you again?' asked Ann.

'I don't think so,' he answered. 'I'm going back to Earth.'

Ann and I found the door in the crater wall. We went into the tunnel and walked downhill for a long way, then went through another air-lock and could take off our spacesuits. It was very warm and the air smelled like . . . what was it?

'It smells like Earth!' Ann said, and she ran forward. 'Kep, come and look!'

In front of us, and to the left and right, were a lot of green plants and small trees. Many of them had flowers and some had fruit on them.

I looked up at the sky. 'Ann, what's keeping out . . . space?' I said.

She laughed. 'I was just thinking that it was clever of them to keep the air *in*. Smell it! Isn't it wonderful? A real earth smell. We're covered by a plastic roof, can you see it?'

'But that's crazy!' I said. 'How can plastic keep out radiation?'

Someone was coming towards us.

'Tim O'Connor!' I said. 'What are *you* doing here?'

He smiled. 'That's the question I was going to ask you. But welcome to Genesis One. You're coming with me, the Boss wants to see you.' He gave each of us a small plastic box. 'Put them on your shirts and don't go out without them.'

'What are they?' I asked. I was sure I had seen them before.

'They're called Nullifiers. We've put a Force Field above the plastic roof to keep radiation out, but the Force Field is dangerous if you're not wearing a Nullifier.'

Then I remembered: Clint and Blue talked about Nullifiers at Aristarchus.

'How long has this place been here, Tim?' Ann was asking. 'And why is it all a secret?'

'Five years,' answered Tim. 'The Boss will explain the rest to you.'

Tim took us into the magical green world and across ground that seemed to be covered with grass – or something that looked like grass. There were buildings in the centre. Tim opened a door and took us down some stairs to a closed door. He knocked.

'Come in!' a voice said.

We went in.

'They're here,' said Tim, and left us there in the doorway.

'Well, Ann, Kep! You *have* been busy, haven't you?'

'Daddy, Daddy!' Ann ran forward and threw her

Tim took us into the magical green world and across ground that seemed to be covered in grass.

arms round Dr Sheppard's neck. I just stood there with my mouth open.

'How did you get here?' Dr Sheppard asked. 'I want to know.'

Together, we told him our story.

Then Ann said, 'But why did you disappear? You've never done it before. I was so worried.'

'I'm sorry, my dear,' said Dr Sheppard. 'It had to be a secret, and this time I had to move quickly.' He looked at me. 'It was after you got back from Aristarchus, Kepler, and told your father that those men in LEMCON had the Genesis Nullifiers. Then we knew somebody from LEMCON was secretly working here in Genesis, so I had to come immediately.'

'You're . . . the Boss?' I asked.

'Yes.'

'And my father knows all about Genesis One?' I said.

'Of course,' he said. 'Genesis One belongs to Moon colony. It's *ours*.'

'Then why is it a big secret?' Ann wanted to know.

'Because we didn't want LEMCON to try to stop us. They don't want us to have our independence, Ann, but we will have it when the UN sees Genesis. *And* when they hear about the things LEMCON have done on Moon.'

'Can Moon really be independent?' asked Ann.

'It's already happening. We can make enough water, air and food for everyone on Moon now. And we can do it cheaper than LEMCON has done it.'

'How exciting!' said Ann. 'Oh, but don't send us back yet, I want to look round at everything.'

'All right,' said her father, with a smile. 'I'll ask Tim to show you.'

'What will happen to Clint and Blue?' I asked.

'Harris will take them back to Earth,' answered Dr Sheppard. 'LEMCON can't be all bad – it sent Harris to find out what is happening here. I've never met Harris, but your father thinks he's a clever man.'

Chapter Six

For the next two days we learned a lot about Genesis.

'I'd really like to live here,' I said, when Ann and I were out walking through the trees.

'I asked my father about that,' said Ann. 'He said, not until we're twenty. And . . . only married people can live in this colony.'

I laughed. 'So how do you feel about getting married?'

'When you came back from Earth, Kep, you were . . . oh, dear, you were very strange and difficult,' she said. 'I didn't think I could marry you.'

'But now?'

'Now you're different.' She smiled.

'You're different too,' I said. And I kissed the end of her nose.

We walked slowly through the green leaves, holding hands . . .

. . . And we knocked into somebody coming towards us!

'Sorry,' I began.

He was an ordinary-looking man, with short hair and blue eyes. His face was the sort that you don't easily remember, but there was a bad cut on the left side of his face. Quickly his hand went up to cover it.

Ann was looking at him. 'It *is* you. Those are the cuts I made on your face. But . . . why are you here? And where's your terrible scar?'

He was lifting his hand to hit her, but I pulled her away.

'Run, Ann!' I shouted. 'Get help, quickly!'

I threw myself between Harris and her, trying to keep away from his hands. I needed time – time for Ann to get help. She ran.

Talk, I thought, make him talk.

He was smiling, but it wasn't a nice smile.

'I thought you were going back to Earth, Harris,' I said.

'My home is here, in Genesis,' he said. 'And my name isn't Harris.'

'So it was *you* who stole the secret of the Force Field and the Nullifiers!' I said. 'But what about Clint and Blue –?'

'They were stupid,' Harris said. 'I didn't need them any more.'

'But if they go back to Earth, they'll talk and –'

'Yes. But they won't go back to Earth. There was an . . . accident.' He smiled again. 'Something went wrong with the air-lock in that garage. When I got back to them, they were dead.'

I felt sick. I knew then that he wanted to kill me too. He had to, or I would talk. 'The UN are coming soon,' I said. 'You can't stop Genesis One now.'

'Stop it?' He looked surprised. 'I don't want to stop it. The people I work for only want to help. LEMCON is finished, but Genesis has a great future. We have money and we want to help with that future.'

42

*Harris immediately pulled the plastic Nullifier off my shirt
and threw it high above the trees.*

'Yes, *criminal* money, dirty money,' I said. 'We don't
want that sort of money, or the control that goes with
it. We don't need it.'

'You will need it,' said Harris. 'I'll make sure of that.'

I got really angry then. 'You –!' I shouted, and ran at
him. I was stupid: he immediately pulled the plastic
Nullifier off my shirt and threw it high above the trees,
then turned and ran the opposite way.

I couldn't believe my luck. He isn't going to kill me! I
thought.

He stopped and looked back, laughing at me. It was
then that I remembered Tim's warning: *the Force Field is
dangerous if you're not wearing a Nullifier.*

So, in about five minutes, Harris will come back and finish me off, I thought. What then? Will Ann know him when the cuts on his face have gone? She saw him without the scar, but only for a few seconds. It was different for me. When you've looked into the eyes of a man who is going to kill you, you never forget him. But already my head was feeling strange, and I fell against a tree.

I could hear his feet coming towards me . . .

I threw myself in among the trees and stayed very still. Slowly my head began to feel better. Why? And then I realized he was so close to me that *his Nullifier was working for both of us.* I waited. Then I saw him – and he saw me!

He came towards me fast, his hands going for my neck. I went straight for his Nullifier, pulled it from his shirt and threw it high, high above the trees.

Then his hands were on my neck. I tried to fight, but slowly, slowly, everything went black.

♦

When I woke up again I was in Kepler Base hospital and my father was looking down at me.

'Did you get Harris?' I was able to whisper.

He smiled. 'Yes. I'm very proud of you, Kep.'

'He killed Clint and Blue. He told me.'

'We found them,' said my father. 'Don't talk any more, Kep. It's all finished. Moon is safe.'

'Ann?'

'You'll see her soon. Now sleep. That's an order.'

So I did.

44

♦

Three weeks later, at midnight, the UN people arrived, and Moon made the first proud move towards independence. LEMCON was closed down, but my father had an idea which he talked to Miles Fargo about. I was with him.

'Why don't *you* keep the mines and miners working, Miles?' he said. 'The colony will pay you and we'll agree on the price to ask Earth for the minerals. But they'll go to people who *need* them, not just people who *want* them.'

'Neither of us will get rich that way, Governor,' answered Miles Fargo.

My father put his hand into his desk and took out a small box. When he opened it the room seemed to shine with a beautiful light.

Miles picked up a shining stone from the box. 'It's wonderful!' he said. 'What is it?'

'It hasn't got a name yet,' said my father. 'But there are a lot of them in Earthdark, ready for mining.'

'Can I mine and sell them?' said Miles Fargo.

'Yes. But only if you agree with my first idea and keep the Aristarchus mines working,' said my father.

'I agree,' said Miles Fargo.

'One other thing,' my father said to Miles. 'I want twelve of the stones for my son's wife. I want to make them into something beautiful for her to wear.'

Miles Fargo smiled. 'I'll be happy to do that.'

When my father and I were alone, he said, 'Was that all right, Kep? You and Ann . . .'

'Yes, father,' I said. 'Everything is going to be all right for Ann and me.'

And it was.

EXERCISES

Vocabulary Work

Some of the words in this book are darker black than others on the page. Do you understand *all* of them? Here are three sentences. Can you finish them, using five of these words?

1 The tourists went to the hotel on the . . .-bus.

2 The man had a . . . on his face.

3 The . . . at Aristarchus were working on Moon because . . . needed Moon's . . .

Comprehension

Chapters 1–2

1 Find the answers to the following questions.
   a Where have Kepler and his father just come from at the start of the story?
   b What is LEMCON's business?
   c Why does Kepler drive to Aristarchus after the sun-storm warning?
   d Why does Clint tell Blue that they must kill Kepler?

Chapters 3–4

2 Who said or thought these words?
   a 'Moon cars usually travel in pairs, it's safer.'
   b 'My father's disappeared.'
   c 'How interesting that the boy seems to know you.'

Chapters 5–6

a   **K** _ _
b   _ _ _ **E** _
c   _ _ _ _ **P** _ _ _
d   _ _ _ **L** _ _ _ _ _ _
e   _ _ _ **E** _ _ _
f   _ _ **R** _ _

3 Make a copy of the above and then read the sentences below to fill in words.

   a Ann uses this short name for Kepler.

   b This is Fargo's first name.

   c This is Ann's last name.

   d Tim gives Kepler and Ann one of these to put on their shirts.

   e This is the first part of the name of the new colony.

   f This sort of Field is used to keep radiation out.

4 Answer these questions.

   a Why is Kepler unhappy to be back on Moon?

   b Why were the people of Kepler Base angry with LEMCON?

   c Why did Kepler and Ann go on the dangerous journey to Earthdark?

   d What was Genesis One?

5 Who said or thought these words?

   a 'We go together, Kep, or we don't go at all.'

   b 'It's food for pigs, this Moon food.'

   c 'They won't wake up for three hours of more.'

Discussion

1 Ann's father did not tell her about Genesis One; he kept it a secret. Was this a good idea?

2 At the end of the story Kepler's father wants Miles Fargo to go on with LEMCON's work in the mines; but he also wants the

minerals to go to the people on Earth who need them, not just the people who want them.

a Would businesses make as much money if they worked this way?

b Would the world be a better place if businesses worked this way?

Writing

1 Use these words to join the following three pairs of sentences together: *and but then*

a We danced silently for a few minutes. I pulled her off the floor.

b My father was sitting behind his desk. He looked very tired.

c I could not hear their voices. I could see almost every word they said.

2 Would you like to live on the moon? Why? Would you make it a better world to live in? How? Give your answers in a report (250 words).